THIS IS LIFE

THIS IS LIFE

An Hachette UK Company
www.hachette.co.uk

Summersdale Publishers Ltd
Part of Octopus Publishing Group Limited
Carmelite House
50 Victoria Embankment
LONDON
EC4Y 0DZ
UK

www.summersdale.com

Printed and bound in China

ISBN: 978-1-78783-530-6

Substantial discounts on bulk quantities of Summersdale books are available to corporations, professional associations and other organizations. For details contact general enquiries: telephone: +44 (0) 1243 771107 or email: enquiries@summersdale.com.

THIS IS LIFE

**BY THE SIBLINGS
HALIL TURAÇTEMUR &
& HAZAN TURAÇTEMUR
ILLUSTRATIONS BY SELIN TAHTAKILIÇ**

summersdale

To

_____

FROM

_____

LIFE IS
a Gift

LIFE IS a ROLLER COASTER

LIFE IS
FOOD

LIFE IS
a BeaCH

LIFE IS
CONFUSING

LIFE IS

LoVe

LIFE IS
a GAME

LIFE IS

LIFE IS Sweet

LIFE IS

a Zoo

LIFE IS
A DaNCe

LIFE IS
A MIRROR

LIFE IS

CRAP

LIFE IS
CRUEL

LIFE IS
GOOD

LIFE IS
a GAMBLE

LIFE IS
A MOVIE

LIFE IS

a STRUGGLE

LIFE IS
a MiRACLE

LIFE IS
ART

LIFE IS
a BATTLE

LIFE IS
SIMPLE

LiFE iS...

_____

ABOUT THE AUTHORS

HAZAN

IS AN ACTRESS, CREATIVE PRODUCER AND GRADUATE OF AMSTERDAM
UNIVERSITY WITH A PASSION FOR THE SUPERNATURAL.

HALIL

WORKS IN GRAPHIC DESIGN, DIGITAL DESIGN AND PHOTOGRAPHY.
HE LOVES TRAVELLING THE WORLD, AND HIS CAT, FUJI.

SELIN

IS AN ILLUSTRATOR AND MASTER'S STUDENT AT MIMAR SINAN FINE ARTS
UNIVERSITY. SHE'S A BIG FAN OF ITALIAN CUISINE AND BEING IN NATURE.

IF YOU'RE INTERESTED IN FINDING OUT MORE ABOUT OUR BOOKS, FIND US ON FACEBOOK AT SUMMERSDALE PUBLISHERS AND FOLLOW US ON TWITTER AT @SUMMERSDALE.

WWW.SUMMERSDALE.COM

HAZAN

IS AN ACTRESS, CREATIVE PRODUCER AND GRADUATE OF AMSTERDAM
UNIVERSITY WITH A PASSION FOR THE SUPERNATURAL.

HALIL

WORKS IN GRAPHIC DESIGN, DIGITAL DESIGN AND PHOTOGRAPHY.
HE LOVES TRAVELLING THE WORLD, AND HIS CAT, FUJI.

SELIN

IS AN ILLUSTRATOR AND MASTER'S STUDENT AT MIMAR SINAN FINE ARTS
UNIVERSITY. SHE'S A BIG FAN OF ITALIAN CUISINE AND BEING IN NATURE.

IF YOU'RE INTERESTED IN FINDING OUT MORE ABOUT OUR BOOKS, FIND US ON FACEBOOK AT SUMMERSDALE PUBLISHERS AND FOLLOW US ON TWITTER AT @SUMMERSDALE.

WWW.SUMMERSDALE.COM